Mind-Bending Lateral Thinking Puzzles

by Des MacHale

Lagoon Books, London

Editor: Heather Dickson
Author: Des MacHale
Additional contributors: Alison Crann, Rosie Atkins
Page design and layout: Linley Clode
Cover design: Gary Inwood Studios

Published by:
LAGOON BOOKS
PO BOX 311, KT2 5QW, U.K.
ISBN 1899712232

Printed in Singapore.

Mind-Bending Lateral Thinking Puzzles

by Des MacHale

LAGOON
BOOKS

INTRODUCTION

This book of Mind-Bending
Lateral Thinking Puzzles was
compiled by Des MacHale,
on behalf of Lagoon Books.
Des MacHale is an Associate
Professor of Mathematics
at University College Cork,
in Ireland. An expert in the
field of lateral thinking,
he has published more than
50 books in a range of subjects
from humour to puzzles.
The cryptic conundrums he
has put together for this book
are designed to trip you
up and catch you out, but
any genius, who is able to
cast logic to the wind
and think laterally, should
be able to crack them.
If you think you're up to it
and want to take up the
challenge, read on.....

Jenny works in a greengrocer's. She only weighed 6 pounds when she was born, but now, aged 18, she is 5 foot 10 inches tall and her measurements are 38 - 24 - 36. What does she weigh?

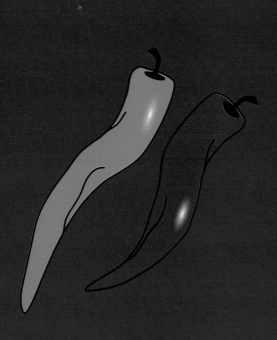

When my watch broke down, I decided to rely on my alarm clock — but it gains a minute every day, so I still didn't know the right time. Was I wrong to swap the stopped watch for the fast clock?

How many famous men and women have been born in New Orleans?

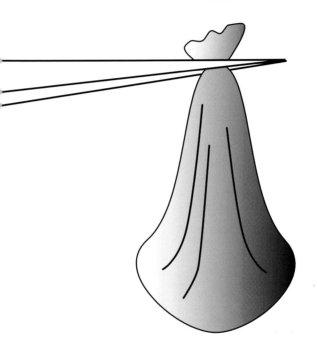

If you buy five pounds of apples, averaging three to the pound, how many apples can you put into an empty paper bag, which will only carry two and a third pounds without bursting?

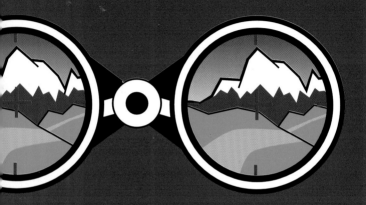

Mount Everest was first climbed in 1953, although its location and height had been recorded long before that in 1841. What was the highest mountain in the world before then?

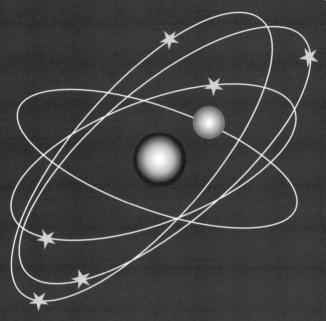

Two of the nearest stars to earth are Sirius, 8.7 light-years away, and Wolf, 7.7 light-years away. Sirius is moving towards us at 8 km per second and Wolf is moving away at 13 km per second. When Wolf has travelled one light-year, what will be the nearest star to the earth?

An electric train is travelling north from Newcastle to Edinburgh, a journey of around 100 miles, at a speed of 75 miles an hour. The wind is blowing from the east at 40 miles an hour. In what direction will the smoke from the train be blown?

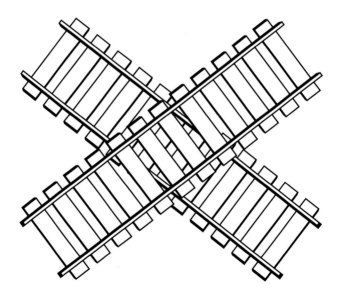

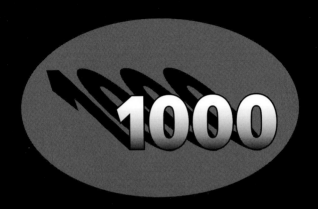

If you multiply 2 by itself a thousand times, what will you get?

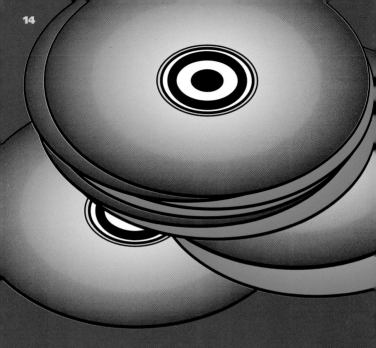

This time last week I was the proud owner of a CD player, a 100 CDs, 20 records and 50 video tapes. On Saturday night I came home to find that a burglar had taken all but ten of the CDs, 12 of the records and 40 of the video tapes. How many CDs have I got left?

What will you find in the centre of Paris, which can't be found in London or Milan?

What form of transport has eight wheels but carries only one passenger?

Who played for both England and France on the same afternoon at Wembley Stadium?

Most English words are quite short, although words of 15 letters or more aren't impossible. What is the longest word in the English language?

The doctor gives you six tablets and tells you to take one every two hours. If you take the first one at 10 am, what time will it be when you take the last one?

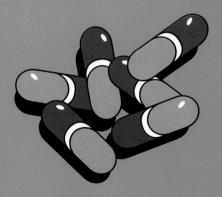

How many times does the letter **'f'** occur in the following sentence?

Friends will not follow your advice if they feel that your words are full of flattery!

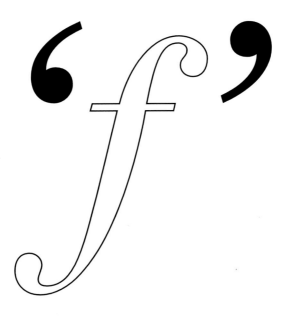

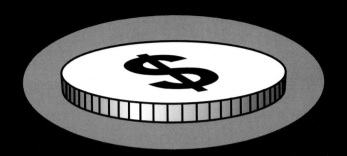

Old coins are usually worth a lot more than their face value, but why are 1989 cents worth almost twenty dollars?

If it takes three minutes to boil one egg in a 2-litre saucepan of salted water, how long will it take to boil three eggs in the saucepan?

If you have a bucket of water (A) at 10 degrees centigrade and another bucket (B) at 10 degrees fahrenheit, and drop a 50 cent coin into each, which coin will be the first to reach the bottom of its bucket?

How many new, uncreased US$10 bills, measuring 5 inches by 2 inches, could you fit without any overlap between pages 33 and 34 of a hardback book measuring 10 inches by 6 inches?

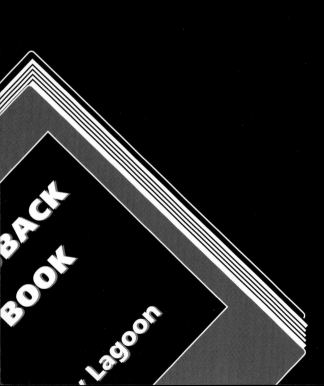

There are four pairs of blue socks and three pairs of red socks in a drawer. In the dark, how many socks must you take out of the drawer to be sure of getting a matching pair?

THOMAS JNR

When Thomas took his dog for a walk, it did not walk in front of him, behind him, above him, below him or to one side of him - and he wasn't carrying it. Where did it walk?

If there were eight crows, on a wall near a sheep pen, and the farmer shot one, how many crows would be left?

In the first week of the Summer harvest Farmer
Jones built six haystacks in one field and five
in another. Each week during the four week-long
harvest, he added six haystacks to each field.
How many piles of hay would he end up with
if, at the end of the harvest, he put them all
together in one field?

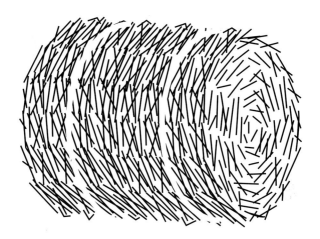

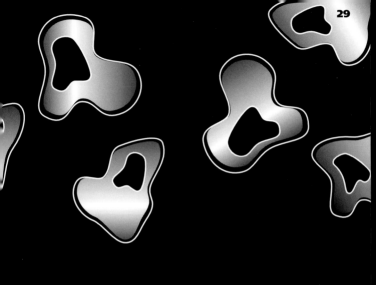

The number of bacteria in a large sealed jar doubles every minute. An hour after the first bacterium was put into the jar and sealed in, the jar is full. When was it half full?

A triangle has three sides, a rectangle has four, a hexagon has six, and so on. How many sides has a circle?

'Two's company and three's a crowd'. What are four and five?

Every time Mary-Jane was late for work, she blamed it on the fact that her watch had stopped and she hadn't known the time. For her birthday, her clever boss bought her a beautiful 14-day watch. How long do you think it would go without her winding it?

1:05 2:18

10:30 9:52

6:37 12:01

Why are so many famous artists Dutch?

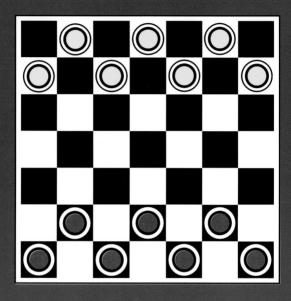

What game begins with a T, has four letters in its name, and is played all over the world?

A woman was born in the Summer of 40BC, and died two months after her 60th birthday. What year did she die in?

The monastic life has all sorts of rules and customs, such as breaking your bread into three pieces as a reminder of the Trinity. Which hand would a monk use to stir his coffee?

Elephants are rarer than they used to be, but they have something to help them survive that no other animal has. What?

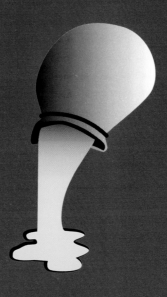

If one man has three sacks of corn on his back, and another has four sacks on his back, which of them has the heavier load?

When the fire alarm sounded in the ten-storey building where he works, Chris didn't bother making for the stairs, but jumped straight out of the nearest window. How did he survive?

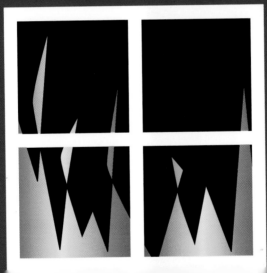

If a tree produces an average of 52 nuts per branch, how many acorns would you expect to find on a gnarled but nevertheless healthy 100-year-old beech tree, with 39 fully grown branches?

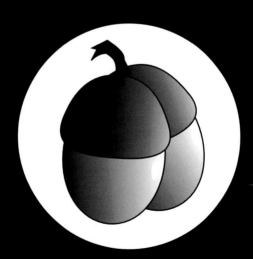

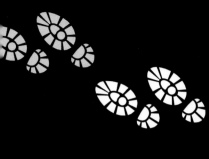

What is the furthest distance you can be from your starting point if you travel exactly five miles south, and then one mile north?

If my friend and I each have the same amount of money, how much should I give her so that she will have US$10 more than I have?

What will you get if you add ten and one four times?

How many letters are there in the alphabet?

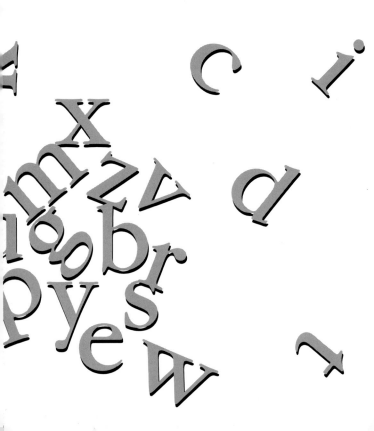

A woman bought a gold ring for US$7,000 and sold it for US$8,000. She later realised that she could get a lot more for it, so she bought it back for US$9,000 and sold it again for US$11,000. What was her total profit?

The verb *'to be'* is unusual in that it has three different singular forms: *'I am'*, *'you are'*, *'he/she/it is'*. Is it ever correct to say *'I is'*?

Even if we never win the Olympics, or get in the Guinness Book of Records, there is one record that each of us holds at one point in our lives; what is it?

Hearing a funny gurgling sound from the kitchen, I went to investigate, and found I had left the water running. The floor was rapidly becoming a miniature sea, and although there were six sponges, a mop and bucket, and a covered floor drain all within reach, I couldn't think what to do first. What should I have done?

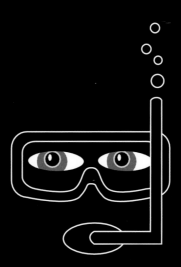

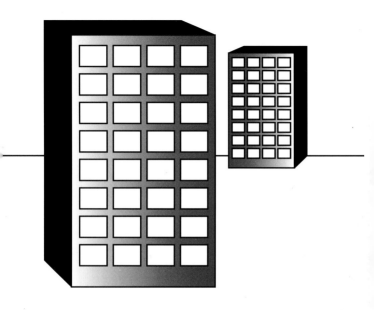

Two adjacent housing estates measure, respectively, four square miles and four miles square. Which is the larger?

Even if every one of these animals were to be destroyed, they would still not be extinct, but would reappear within a few months.
What are they?

When a friend came to stay recently, I knocked on her door one morning and asked her a question. She said 'Yes', so I knew she was lying. What was my question?

If the first third of an atlas shows Europe and Africa, the second third shows the Americas, and the last part shows everywhere else, in which section will you find the Islets of Langerhans?

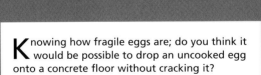

Knowing how fragile eggs are; do you think it would be possible to drop an uncooked egg onto a concrete floor without cracking it?

A donkey was tied to a 20-foot rope. How did it manage to eat a pile of hay 50 feet away without biting through the rope?

What is the difference between an old, crumpled and slightly torn ten dollar bill and a new one?

What is filled in the morning and emptied at night, except for one night of the year when it is filled at night and emptied in the morning?

What do you get if you divide 40 by a half and add 10 to the result?

The Caliph of Baghdad was once approached by a man who offered to sell him a flask of universal solvent - a liquid that he swore would dissolve any substance it touched. The Caliph knew as soon as he saw the flask that the man was lying. How did he know?

Which would burn longer, a short fat blue candle or a long thin spirally yellow one?

Which of the states in the USA is round at both ends and high in the middle?

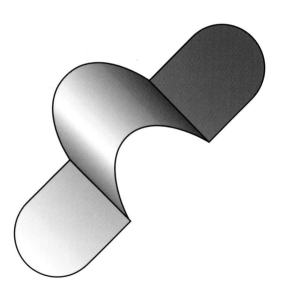

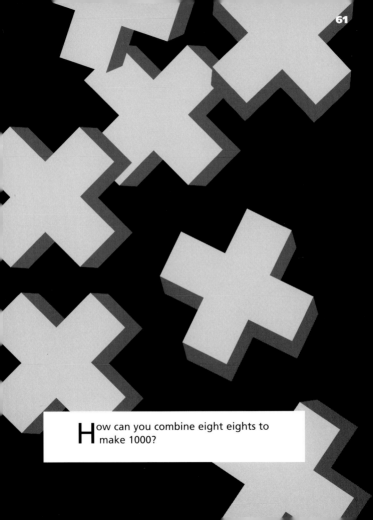

How can you combine eight eights to make 1000?

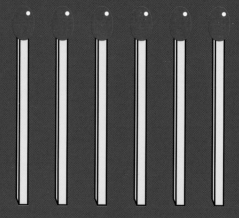

Can you make four equal triangles using six matchsticks, without breaking them or bending them?

I have trouble telling my left hand from my right, so I bought a pair of reversible gloves, red on one side and blue on the other. I put a red glove on my right hand, and turned the other one inside out so that my left hand would be blue - but it didn't work. What went wrong?

Is there anything from which you can take away the whole and still have some left?

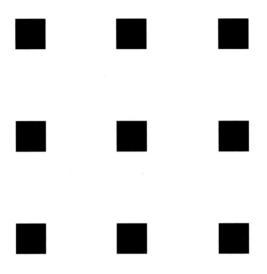

hat is the minimum number of straight lines which will connect all the dots?

Mr Smith eats two eggs every day. He never buys any eggs, nobody gives them to him, he doesn't steal them from anyone and he doesn't keep hens. Where does he get his eggs from?

What would happen if you struck a match in a room filled with hydrogen gas?

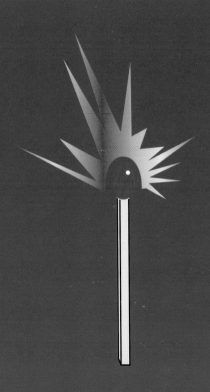

A boy was asked to multiply five numbers together. He was shown each number in turn, but before even seeing the last two numbers, he gave the correct answer. How did he do it?

How quickly can you find out what is unusual about this paragraph? It looks so ordinary that you would think nothing was wrong with it at all - and in fact nothing is wrong, it's just distinctly odd. Go to work on it and try your skill!

John and Jim fell asleep on their airbeds on the beach, and got swept out to sea. John was nearly saved, but Jim was nearly drowned. Which of them later donated a week's wages to the Lifeboat Institute?

There is a short story which describes the end of Time and its reversal, with people living backwards from the grave to the cradle. Other than in fiction, where would August come before July?

What is the capital of Antarctica?

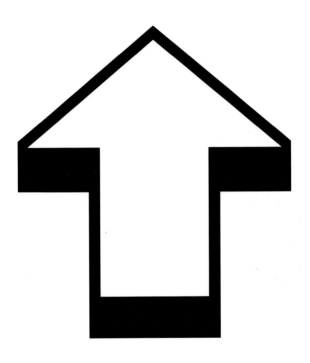

In what sport do all the players except one move backwards?

If the average eskimo eats 10 walruses in a lifetime, and one walrus is equivalent to five and a half penguins, how many penguins would he eat if he couldn't get walruses?

What is twice two thirds of three quarters of ten?

A man is ship-wrecked on a desert island. The only thing he has in his possession are a flint, a can of lighter fuel, a penknife and a packet of cigarettes. How could he make a cigarette lighter?

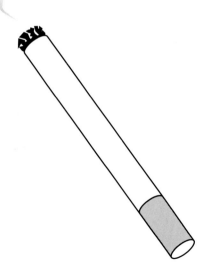

In general, the older a coin is, the greater its value. Which would be worth more, a British silver penny with the date 1453, or a Greek silver obol with the date 453 BC?

What is as big as a hippopotamus, the same shape as a hippopotamus, but weighs a lot less than a hippopotamus?

*A*fter passing her driving test, Sally was on her way home, feeling very pleased with herself and not really concentrating on where she was going. She went straight over a zebra crossing and the wrong way up a one-way street. Her driving instructor and a passing policeman saw her, but didn't bat an eyelid. Why?

*A*merican law varies from state to state, especially as regards basics such as birth, marriage and death; can a man living in Texas be legally buried in Hawaii?

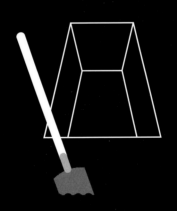

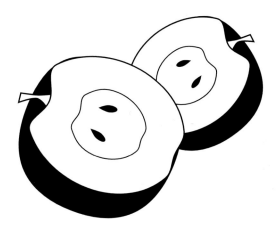

When asked which half of an apple he would like, 11-year-old Peter replied *"the bigger half"*; on hearing this, his 12-year-old sister Pauline — who had been learning all about superlatives at school that day - retorted *"You mean, the biggest half"*. Who was correct?

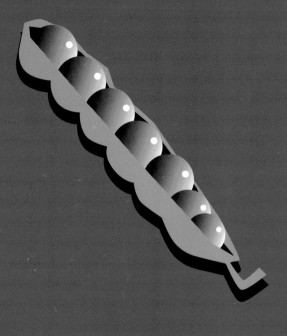

How many peas are there in a pod?

^{D}ave was trying to match four different coloured pairs of socks which had come out of the washing machine. There was a blue pair, a red pair, a green pair and a yellow pair. Unfortunately he is completely colour blind and could not differentiate between them, so he paired them randomly. What is the probability that exactly three pairs matched?

Believe it or not, there's something in London, which can also be seen in France and New York. What is it?

A man went into a cafe, sat down and ordered a black cup of coffee, a glass of orange juice and a Danish pastry. "Ah," said the waitress, "You must be a policeman". How did she know?

While travelling up the Amazon, an explorer noticed an ostrich egg floating downstream. Where would it have come from?

When the police arrested a suspected murderer, they found a blood-stained knife in the outside right pocket of his jacket. The next day, when they went to get the evidence, they found the knife in the inside left pocket of his jacket. Nobody had touched the jacket - as it was locked away - so how did the knife end up in a different place?

page 6
Fruit and vegetables.

page 7
No - the watch will tell you the correct time twice a day but you can't tell when, whereas the alarm clock will gain a minute every day but at least you can work out by how much it is wrong.

page 8
None - they were babies when they were born.

page 9
Only one - after the first apple, the bag is no longer empty.

page 10
Mount Everest - the discovery didn't change its height.

page 11
The sun - it will always be the closest star to the earth whatever the movements of other stars.

page 12
It won't - electric trains don't produce smoke.

page 13
Four - it doesn't matter how many times you do the sum, 2 x 2 will always equal 4.

page 14
Ten.

page 15
The letter R.

page 16
A pair of roller skates.

page 17
The band - they played the national anthems for both teams.

page 18
The longest word in the phrase 'the English language' is 'language'.

page 19
It will be 8 pm.

page 20
There are seven:
Friends will not **f**ollow

your advice if they feel
that your words are full of
flattery!

page 21
Because 1989 cents comes
to US$19.89 - the number
referred to the quantity,
not the date.

page 22
Three minutes - the pan is
large enough to cook them
all together.

page 23
The one in bucket A; 10
degrees fahrenheit is
below freezing, so the coin
in bucket B will just sit on
the ice.

page 24
None - pages 33 and 34 are
always two sides of the
same leaf.

page 25
Three. Each sock could
be either red or blue;
even if the first two are
different colours, the third
will have to match one
or the other.

page 26
If the dog isn't in front,
behind, above, below or
on one side, then it must
be on Thomas's other side.

page 27
One - the dead one; the
rest would have flown
away.

page 28
If he put all the haystacks
together, they would make
one large pile.

page 29
At one minute before
the hour.

page 30
Two - the inside and
the outside.

page 31
Nine - 4+5=9.

page 32
It won't go at all
without winding.

page 33
Because they were born
in Holland.

page 34
Golf - the first thing you do is put the ball on a Tee!

page 35
21 AD - the numbering goes from 1 BC to 1 AD.

page 36
Neither; he would use a spoon.

page 37
Baby elephants.

page 38
The first; three sacks of corn are heavier than four empty sacks.

page 39
It was a ground floor window.

page 40
None; acorns grow on oak trees.

page 41
6 miles - if you are 5 miles north of the south pole, you can travel south to the pole and carry on in the same direction for another one mile ending up 6 miles from your starting point.

page 42
US$5. If we both start with US$20, and I give her US$5, she will have US$25 and I will be left with US$15.

page 43
11 each time.

page 44
Eleven - T H E A L P H A B E T.

page 45
US$3,000; US$1,000 on the first sale and US$2,000 on the second.

page 46
Yes - 'I is the ninth letter of the alphabet'.

page 47
Being the youngest person in the world.

page 48
Turned off the tap.

page 49
Four miles square; the area is four miles on each side,

which is 16 square miles.

page 50
Mules; they're a cross
between a horse and
a donkey.

page 51
'Are you asleep?'

page 52
You won't; they are part of
the pancreas.

page 53
Yes - it would be
impossible to crack a
concrete floor with an egg.

page 54
The other end of the rope
wasn't attached to
anything.

page 55
The difference between a
ten-dollar bill and a one-
dollar bill is nine dollars.

page 56
A stocking (or sock) that's
hung up on Christmas Eve.

page 57
90.
$40 \div 1/2 = 80$, $80 + 10 = 90$.

page 58
The liquid hadn't dissolved
the flask.

page 59
Neither - candles burn
shorter.

page 60
OHIO.

page 61
Here are two ways:
$8 + 8 + 8 + 88 + 888 = 1000$.
$$\frac{8888 - 888}{8} = 1000.$$
Can you find any others?

page 62
Form them into a pyramid
with three triangular sides
and a triangular base, using
three for the base and one
rising from each
corner to meet
above the
centre.

page 63

If you turn a glove inside out, it fits the opposite hand, so when I turned my left-hand red glove to show blue, it became a right-hand glove.

page 64

The word 'wholesome'.

page 65

Four.

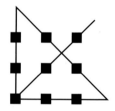

page 66

He keeps ducks.

page 67

Nothing - the match couldn't burn if there was no oxygen in the room.

page 68

The third number was zero, so the final answer had to be zero no matter what other numbers were included.

page 69

There is no 'e' in any of the words, in spite of the fact that it is the most common letter in the English language.

page 70

Jim; he was nearly drowned but actually saved, whereas John was nearly saved but actually drowned.

page 71

In the dictionary.

page 72

The letter 'A'.

page 73

Rowing - the oarsmen face the stern of the boat and therefore move backwards, while the cox faces the bow and moves forwards.

page 74

None; eskimos live in the

Arctic, penguins live near the Antarctic.

page 75
Ten. Two thirds of three quarters is two quarters (a half) and twice a half is a whole, 1 x 10 = 10.

page 76
He could take some tobacco out of it.

page 77
The penny; the obol would be a fake, as no-one in 453 BC could have foreseen the Christian dating system.

page 78
Its shadow.

page 79
She was returning home on foot.

page 80
Not while he's still alive.

page 81
Neither - if something is cut in half, both halves are the same size.

page 82
There is one P in 'a pod'.

page 83
Zero. If three pairs match the fourth one does too.

page 84
The letter N.

page 85
He was wearing his uniform.

page 86
An ostrich.

page 87
It didn't. The jacket was reversible and when the villain took his coat off, it had turned inside out, making the outside right pocket the inside left.

FURTHER READING:

Mind-Bending Lateral Thinking Puzzles
(Lagoon Books, 1994)

Mind-Bending Lateral Thinking Puzzles - Volume II
(Lagoon Books, 1996)

Lateral Thinking Puzzles - A Cocktail of Conundrums for Connoisseurs
(Lagoon Books, 1996)

Challenging Lateral Thinking Puzzles by Paul Sloane and Des MacHale
(Sterling Publishing, 1992)

LAGOON
BOOKS